宇宙小子

【美】劳拉·德里斯科尔◎著

【美】瑞贝卡·桑伯罗◎

范晓星◎译

天津出版传媒集团

新蕾出版社

图书在版编目 (CIP) 数据

宇宙小子/(美)德里斯科尔(Driscoll,L.)著;
(美)桑伯罗(Thornburgh,R.)绘;范晓星译.——天津:
新蕾出版社,2015.11(2024.12 重印)
(数学帮帮忙·互动版)
书名原文:The Blast Off Kid
ISBN 978-7-5307-6308-7

Ⅰ.①宇… Ⅱ.①德… ②桑… ③范… Ⅲ.①数学–
儿童读物 Ⅳ.①O1–49

中国版本图书馆 CIP 数据核字(2015)第 238369 号

出版发行: 天津出版传媒集团
新蕾出版社
http://www.newbuds.com.cn
地　　址: 天津市和平区西康路 35 号(300051)
出 版 人: 马玉秀
电　　话: 总编办 (022)23332422
发行部 (022)23332679　23332351
传　　真: (022)23332422
经　　销: 全国新华书店
印　　刷: 天津新华印务有限公司
开　　本: 787mm×1092mm　1/16
印　　张: 3
版　　次: 2015 年 11 月第 1 版　2024 年 12 月第 24 次印刷
定　　价: 12.00 元

无处不在的数学

资深编辑　卢　江

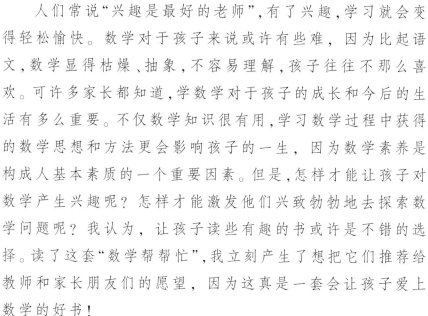

　　人们常说"兴趣是最好的老师"，有了兴趣，学习就会变得轻松愉快。数学对于孩子来说或许有些难，因为比起语文，数学显得枯燥、抽象，不容易理解，孩子往往不那么喜欢。可许多家长都知道，学数学对于孩子的成长和今后的生活有多么重要。不仅数学知识很有用，学习数学过程中获得的数学思想和方法更会影响孩子的一生，因为数学素养是构成人基本素质的一个重要因素。但是，怎样才能让孩子对数学产生兴趣呢？怎样才能激发他们兴致勃勃地去探索数学问题呢？我认为，让孩子读些有趣的书或许是不错的选择。读了这套"数学帮帮忙"，我立刻产生了想把它们推荐给教师和家长朋友们的愿望，因为这真是一套会让孩子爱上数学的好书！

　　这套有趣的图书从美国引进，原出版者是美国资深教育专家。每本书讲述一个孩子们生活中的故事，由故事中出现的问题自然地引入一个数学知识，然后通过运用数学知识解决问题。比如，从帮助外婆整理散落的纽扣引出分类，从为小狗记录藏骨头的地点引出空间方位等等。故事素材全部来源于孩子们的真实生活，不是童话，不是幻想，而是鲜活的生活实例。正是这些发生在孩子身边的故事，让孩子们懂得，数学无处不在并且非常有用；这些鲜活的实例也使得抽象的概念更易于理解，更容易激发孩子学习数学的兴趣，让他们逐渐爱上数学。这样的教育思想和方法与我国近年来提倡的数学教育理念是十分吻合的！

这是一套适合 5~8 岁孩子阅读的书，书中的有趣情节和生动的插画可以将抽象的数学问题直观化、形象化，为孩子的思维活动提供具体形象的支持。如果亲子共读的话，家长可以带领孩子推测情节的发展，探讨解决难题的办法，让孩子在愉悦的氛围中学到知识和方法。

值得教师和家长朋友们注意的是，在每本书的后面，出版者还加入了"互动课堂"及"互动练习"，一方面通过一些精心设计的活动让孩子巩固新学到的数学知识，进一步体会知识的含义和实际应用；另一方面帮助家长指导孩子阅读，体会故事中数学之外的道理，逐步提升孩子的阅读理解能力。

我相信孩子读过这套书后一定会明白，原来，数学不是烦恼，不是包袱，数学真能帮大忙！

每天，吉姆都带午饭去上学。每天，他的午饭都是老三样：三明治、苹果和一块宇宙小子牌能量棒。

吉姆很喜欢吃宇宙小子牌能量棒。

吉姆的好朋友艾弗雷特和雷切尔也喜欢吃这种能量棒，可没有吉姆那么喜欢。吉姆把每种口味都尝了个遍，可他自己也说不清最喜欢哪种口味。

　　吉姆咬了一口能量棒。嗯！摩卡口味的！

　　吉姆也爱看这种能量棒的广告。

　　在广告里，总有那么一位宇航员在太空漫步。他说:"宇宙小子能量棒! 冲向宇宙!"

　　有一天，吉姆正津津有味地嚼着一块可可味儿的宇宙小子能量棒时，被包装纸上的字吸引住了。

　　不可能！太空夏令营？只要收集些能量棒的包装纸？

　　吉姆仔细看了看下面一行小字：只要集齐10000张包装纸，就能参加太空夏令营！

　　虽然这行字很小很小，可这个数字却不小，简直遥不可及！

　　这天晚上，吉姆梦见自己身穿宇航服，在失重状态下飘浮。他手里攥着一块宇宙小子能量棒，那是专为太空之旅而冷冻干燥过的能量棒呢。他一边飘来飘去，一边念念有词："宇宙小子能量棒！冲向宇宙！"

早餐的时候，吉姆吃了一块宇宙小子能量棒，是草莓口味的。吃完以后，他把包装纸整理得平平整整，然后夹进背包里。

　　午餐的时候他也这样做，那一周天天如此。

周五，吉姆数了数他的包装纸。

"才 10 个呀！"他失望地对艾弗雷特说。

吉姆不清楚他到底差几张，但他知道差得还很远。

从那以后，艾弗雷特每天把自己攒下的宇宙小子能量棒包装纸都交给吉姆，雷切尔也是。

　　周二，一个四年级的同学走到吉姆身边停了下来，问道：“你是不是那个‘宇宙小子’？”

　　“可能就是我吧。”吉姆答道。

　　于是，这个女孩把她午餐桌上攒到的包装纸也都给了吉姆。

　　“谢谢你！”吉姆说，“消息传得真快呀！”

又到周五了，吉姆的背包里已经塞满了包装纸。他都不知道自己到底有多少张了，因为他每数一次，结果都不一样。

"我明白了。"吉姆说，"我把这些包装纸 10 张一摞用曲别针夹好，这样想看我有多少张包装纸就很容易了。"

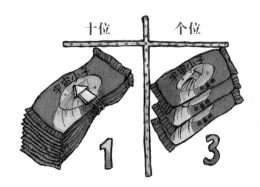

十位　　　个位

周一有校会。校长讲的是校内安全问题。然后，有两位同学上前通知了几件事。这启发了吉姆，他写了一张小纸条，递到了校长手里。

松树岭
小学

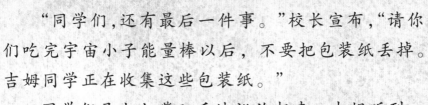

　　"同学们，还有最后一件事。"校长宣布，"请你们吃完宇宙小子能量棒以后，不要把包装纸丢掉。吉姆同学正在收集这些包装纸。"

　　同学们马上七嘴八舌地议论起来。吉姆听到一个女孩说："宇宙小子！"然后，大笑起来。呃……他觉得很不好意思。

宠物毛失，
请帮忙找到
我的小猫奥奥。

可这一切都是值得的。那天吃过午餐，吉姆的背包又装了满满一书包的包装纸。

第二天也是……以后每天都是。

　　周五，雷切尔和艾弗雷特帮吉姆数一摞摞的包装纸。艾弗雷特说："数得我眼都花了。"

　　"我也是！"雷切尔说。

　　"等一下。"吉姆说，"我去拿些购物袋来，咱们把每 10 摞放进一个袋里。"

  没多久，他们装好了 4 个购物袋，每个袋里都有 100 张包装纸。除此以外，还剩下 2 摞零 5 张包装纸。

  "一共有 425 张！"雷切尔说道。

  "哇！"艾弗雷特说，"你那天的通知有效果啦！"

  吉姆心想：艾弗雷特说得没错，广告的力量真强大！我要再宣传宣传！

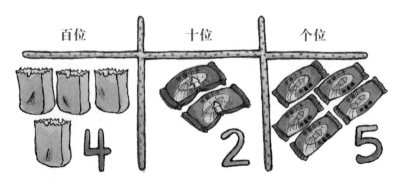

那个周末，吉姆真的这样做了。他写了很多小广告，先在杂货店的告示栏上贴了一张，还在那里放了一个收集包装纸的空盒子。接着，他在网吧、录像店、健身房也都做了同样的事情。

一周后，一位阿姨从健身房给吉姆打来电话。"请你赶快来把这些包装纸拿走好吗？"她说，"前台都快放不下啦！"

宇宙小子
包装纸

超级减肥
☆健身舞☆
报名从速！

吉姆很理解健身房老板的苦恼，因为他
自己的房间也已经堆满了包装纸！

"吉姆！"妈妈从门外探进头来喊他，"你
在屋里吗？"

"我在呢，妈妈！"吉姆答道。他的声音从
床后什么地方传来。

　　吉姆和妈妈把收集的包装纸搬到车库。他们找来了垃圾袋，把每十个购物袋装进一个垃圾袋。等他们装完一数，总共 6 个大垃圾袋。

　　除了那些，他们还剩 3 个购物袋，5 摞曲别针夹好的和 4 张零散的包装纸。

　　"一共是 6354 张包装纸！"吉姆兴奋地喊道。

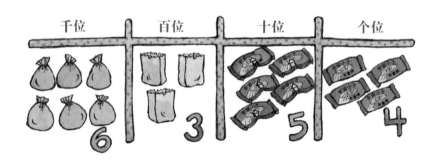

千位	百位	十位	个位
6	3	5	4

周六下午，一位报社记者敲响了吉姆家的门。"请问你是吉姆吗？是那个'宇宙小子'吗？我看到城里到处都是你贴的广告呢。"

第二天早晨，吉姆翻开了报纸……

他上报了!

没多久,吉姆开始收到来信。第一天只有 6 封。

可是转天就有 12 封了!

接下来的一周，邮递员叔叔每天都专程到吉姆家，他的车上全都是给宇宙小子寄来的包装纸！

周三，吉姆的爸爸正要去上班时问道："谁见着我的车钥匙了？"吉姆的妈妈在厨房找到了。

　　"谢谢。"吉姆的爸爸说完，打开车库的门又问，"呃……谁见着我的车了？"

"这儿到底有多少包装纸？"吉姆的爸爸接着问道,他们把袋子挪开,露出车子,开始数起包装纸来。

总共有 9 个大垃圾袋,9 个购物袋,9 小撮曲别针夹好的和 9 张零散的。吉姆惊讶得合不拢嘴:"这就是说……"

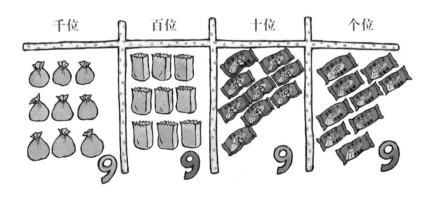

千位	百位	十位	个位
9	9	9	9

吉姆冲进屋，他选了一块葡萄口味的宇宙小子能量棒，一把撕开包装纸。

他把这张包装纸和另外那 9 张零散的合在一起，刚好凑上一摞 10 张。现在，他有 10 摞曲别针夹好的了。

他把这些放进了一个购物袋。现在，他有 10 个装满的购物袋。他把这些购物袋装进了一个大垃圾袋。他有 10 个刚刚装满的垃圾袋了！

"我集到 10000 张包装纸啦！"吉姆喊道。

　　吉姆的妈妈给宇宙小子能量棒公司打了一个电话，过了一个月，吉姆真的来到了太空夏令营！

　　吉姆给家里写了一张明信片。

亲爱的爸爸妈妈：

　　我在太空夏令营特别开心。

今天，我学习了火箭的知识。

昨天，我尝试了模拟飞行。

明天，我还会坐上失重椅！

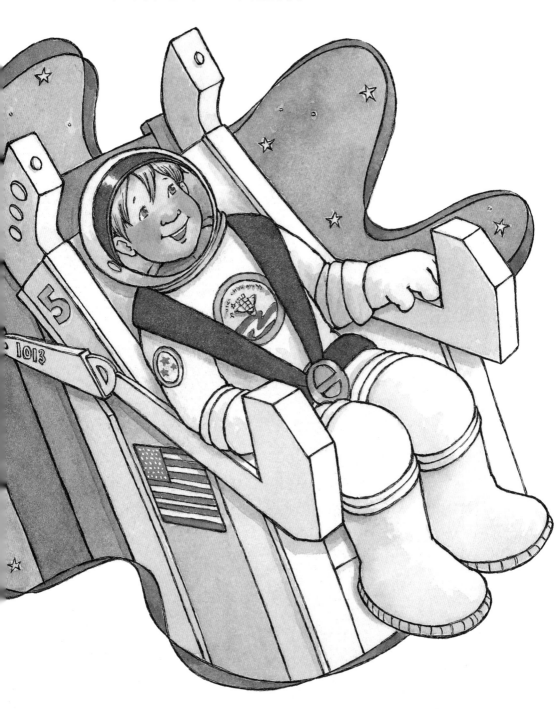

啊，太棒啦！而且，我还可以带很多很多宇宙小子能量棒回家呢！我要把这些能量棒分给所有帮助我实现梦想的人。我爱你们！

另：请不要丢掉宇宙小子能量饮料的瓶盖哟！我听说，他们还有新一轮的大奖活动呢！

吉姆

位值制计数法

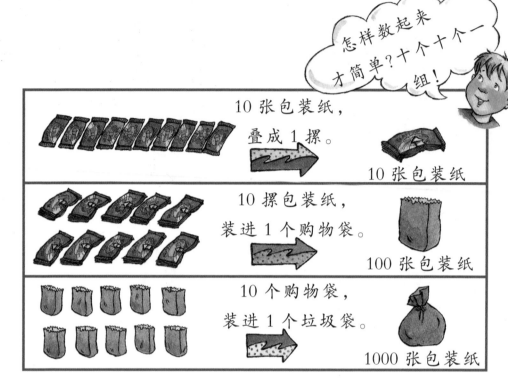

10 张包装纸，叠成 1 摞。

10 张包装纸

10 摞包装纸，装进 1 个购物袋。

100 张包装纸

10 个购物袋，装进 1 个垃圾袋。

1000 张包装纸

位值图可以让你知道怎样读写数字。

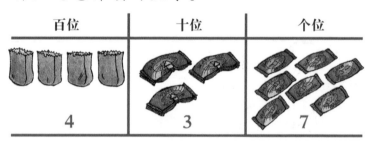

百位	十位	个位
4	3	7

四百三十七

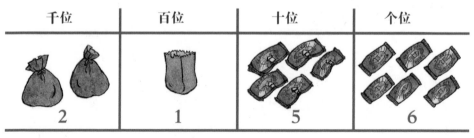

千位	百位	十位	个位
2	1	5	6

两千一百五十六

亲爱的家长朋友，请您和孩子一起完成下面这些内容，会有更大的收获哟！

提高阅读能力

• 阅读封面，包括书名、作者等内容。和孩子聊聊封面上的这个男孩为什么有那么多包装纸呢？"宇宙小子"是什么意思？

• 和孩子一起读故事，重温第 11，15，20 页，请孩子想一想，吉姆为什么想把包装纸用曲别针夹起来，变成一摞一摞的呢？又为什么把一摞摞的包装纸，放进购物袋，最后又分装进垃圾袋呢？

• 吉姆说要怎样感谢那些帮助他赢得大奖的人呢？

巩固数学概念

• 请根据第 32 页上的内容，让孩子说一说，哪组的包装纸多？是用曲别针夹起来的多呢，还是装进购物袋里的多呢？15 张包装纸多，还是曲别针夹起来的一摞多？8 摞这样的包装纸多，还是一整个购物袋里的多？一个垃圾袋里的包装纸多，还是 12 个购物袋里的包装纸多？

• 请家长出题，让孩子自己动脑筋想想。比如，吉姆有 1548 张包装纸，可以装几个垃圾袋？几个购物袋？几摞用曲别针夹起来的？几张零散的？

• 在第 25 页上，吉姆已经积攒了 9999 张包装纸。问问孩子，每个 9 各代表什么。（提示：最右边的 9 代表 9 个 1）

• 请用绘图格纸，剪下 10×10 见方的纸板。用这张纸板来跟孩子学习如何进位。首先，将纸板剪成 10 条，再把每条剪成 10 个小方块。请孩子用 10 个小方块，拼成一个长条，再将 10 个长条拼成完整的正方形。问问孩子：多少个小方块可以组成一个长条，多少个 1 组成 10？多少个长条可以组成一个正方形？多少个 10 可以组成 100？

【答案：均为 10】

生活中的数学

　　将一张 A4 纸折成 4 等份。从左到右分别写上：千位、百位、十位、个位。剪 10 张小卡片，分别写上 0~9 的 10 个数字。家长说出一个数字，让孩子将卡片放在对应的位值上。例如：四位数 2648 应怎样摆呢？8241 的百位上的数字是多少呢？3150 有几个 1000？几个 100？几个 10？

吉姆和小伙伴们为了参加宇宙小子公司举办的新一轮的大奖活动，开始收集宇宙小子能量饮料的瓶盖。看看他们都收集了多少个？

哪一位空缺，请以 0 占位，若最高位空缺，则不能写 0。

百位	十位	个位

写作：_____
读作：_____

百位	十位	个位

写作：_____
读作：_____

百位	十位	个位

写作：_____
读作：_____

百位	十位	个位

写作：_____
读作：_____

百位	十位	个位

写作：_____
读作：_____

35

互动练习2

每 100 个瓶盖可换得一个宇航员的玩偶。吉姆和小伙伴们一共可以换得多少个玩偶呢?

	百位	十位	个位
	100个	10个 10个 10个 10个 10个	(4个瓶盖)
		10个 10个 10个 10个 10个 10个	(8个瓶盖)
	100个 100个		(10个瓶盖)
		10个 10个 10个 10个 10个 10个 10个	(6个瓶盖)
	100个 100个 100个	10个 10个 10个 10个 10个 10个 10个	(6个瓶盖)

6 个 [100个]　　　27 个 [10个]　　　34 个 (瓶盖)

10 个 [10个] 相当于 1 个 [100个]　　10 个 (瓶盖) 相当于 1 个 [10个]

① (　) 个 [100个] +(　) 个 [10个]　② (　) 个 [10个] +(　) 个 (瓶盖)

③ (　) 个 [100个]

④ 一共可以换得(　) 个玩偶。

36

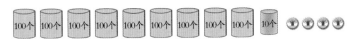

吉姆和小伙伴们已经收集了 914 个瓶盖，他们还要收集多少个瓶盖才能达到 1000 个？

再收集（　）个瓶盖，个位上就满 10 了，可以将 10 个 ⬤ 装在 1 个新的蓝桶里。此时，总数就达到（　）个。

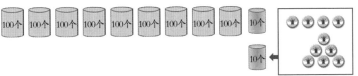

再收集（　）个瓶盖，十位上也能满 10 了，可以将 10 个 10个 装在一个新的黄桶里。

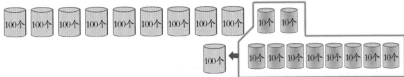

黄桶也满 10 个了，10 个 100 就是 1000，需要装在更大的红桶里。

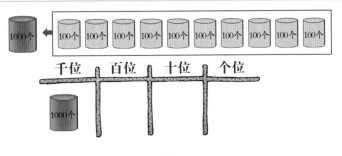

千位　　百位　　十位　　个位

写作：＿＿＿＿＿　读作：＿＿＿＿＿

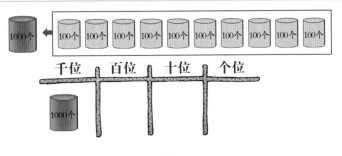

37

吉姆和小伙伴们已经收集了 1000 个瓶盖，只要继续努力，集齐 10000 个瓶盖，就能参加第二期的太空夏令营了。他们还差（　　）个呢？

吉姆他们在各个场所都放置了收集瓶盖的纸盒。快来帮他们数数各个纸盒里瓶盖的数量吧。

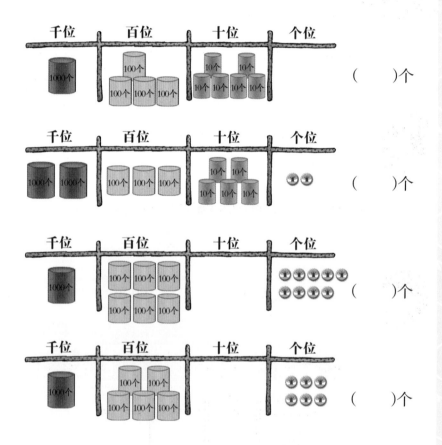

上述四个纸盒中的瓶盖加在一起，一共有（　　）个。

通过大家的帮助,吉姆他们离目标越来越近,快来看看他们已经收集了多少个瓶盖。

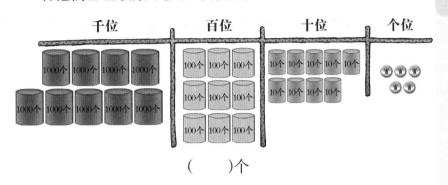

( )个

10 个 1000 是 10000,吉姆他们还差多少个瓶盖就能实现目标了呢? 快在下面的进位图中将缺少的瓶盖补充上吧。

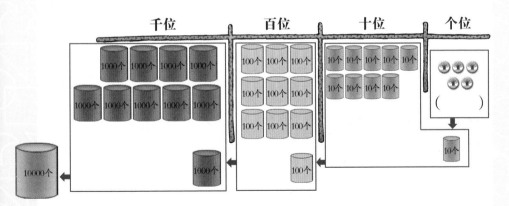

吉姆他们终于集齐了 10000 个瓶盖,下面我们来仔细学习下这些数位。

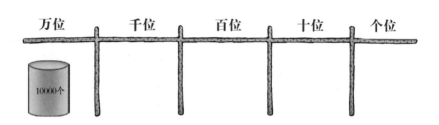

写作:_____ 读作:_____

下面,我们通过收集瓶盖的过程来学习各位数的进制关系。

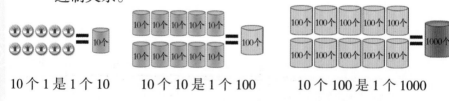

10 个 1 是 1 个 10　　　10 个 10 是 1 个 100　　　10 个 100 是 1 个 1000

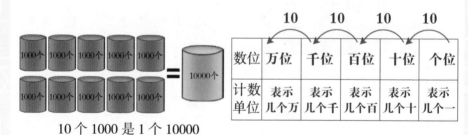

10 个 1000 是 1 个 10000

数位	万位	千位	百位	十位	个位
计数单位	表示几个万	表示几个千	表示几个百	表示几个十	表示几个一

相邻的两个计数单位间的进率是( )。

在数学教学中,我们通常用"计数器"表示各个数位上的数。请根据前面我们学习的知识,来回答下列各题。

( )个万( )个千( )个百( )个十( )个一

写作:＿＿＿＿＿＿＿

读作:＿＿＿＿＿＿＿

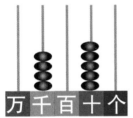

( )个万( )个千( )个百( )个十( )个一

写作:＿＿＿＿＿＿＿

读作:＿＿＿＿＿＿＿

( )个万( )个千( )个百( )个十( )个一

写作:＿＿＿＿＿＿＿

读作:＿＿＿＿＿＿＿

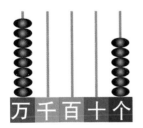

( )个万( )个千( )个百( )个十( )个一

写作:＿＿＿＿＿＿＿

读作:＿＿＿＿＿＿＿

参考答案

互动练习1：
154，一百五十四
68，六十八
209，二百零九
76，七十六
397，三百九十七

互动练习2：
① 2,7
② 3,4
③ 1
④ 9

互动练习3：
6, 920
80
1000，一千

互动练习4：
9000
1460
2352
1609
1506
6927

互动练习5：
9995

互动练习6：
10000，一万
10

互动练习7：
0,3, 1, 2, 6
3126   三千一百二十六

0, 4, 0, 5, 0
4050   四千零五十

1,4,2,7,3
14273   一万四千二百七十三

8,0,0,0,6
80006   八万零六

（习题设计:董惠平　鹿　美）

THE BLAST OFF KID

Every day Jim brought his lunch to school. And every day, it was the same—a sandwich, an apple, and a Blast Off Energy Bar.

Jim loved Blast Off Bars.

Jim's friends Everett and Rachel liked Blast Off Bars, too. But not the way Jim did. He had tried every single flavor. He couldn't decide which one he liked best.

Jim took a bite of his bar. Mmm! Mocha Chip!

Jim even liked the ads on TV.

There was always the same astronaut doing a spacewalk. He would say, "Blast Off Energy Bars—they're out of this world!"

One day Jim was munching on a Cocoa Blast Off Bar.

Something on the wrapper caught his eye.

No way! A trip to space camp? Just for saving a few wrappers? Then he checked the fine print:

You need just 10000 wrappers to win!

Even in tiny print, that was one big number—an impossible number.

That night Jim dreamed he was wearing a space suit and floating in zero gravity. He was holding a Blast Off Bar—freeze-dried for space. And he was saying, "Blast Off Bars—they're out of this world!"

At breakfast, Jim had a Strawberry Blast Off Bar. When he was finished, he smoothed out the empty wrapper. Then he tucked it into his backpack.

He did the same thing at lunch that day, and every day that week.

Jim counted his wrappers on Friday.

"Only ten?" he moaned to Everett.

Jim wasn't sure how many more he needed. But he knew it was a lot.

From then on, Everett gave all his Blast Off wrappers to Jim. So did Rachel.

Oh Tuesday, one of the fourth graders stopped by. "Are you the Blast Off Kid?" she asked.

"I guess I am," Jim replied.

She handed him the wrappers from her lunch table.

"Thanks!" said Jim. "News travels fast."

By Friday, Jim's backpack was stuffed with wrappers. He didn't even know how many he had. Each time he counted, he got a different number.

"I know," Jim said. "I'll use paper clips to put the wrappers in bundles of ten. Then it will be easy to see how many I have."

There was an assembly on Monday. The principal talked about school safety. Then two kids made announcements. That gave Jim an idea. He scribbled a note and brought it up to the principal.

"Students, one last thing," the principal said. "Please don't throw away your Blast Off Bar wrappers. Jim is collecting them."

A ripple of chatter went through the crowd. Jim heard a girl say, "Blast Off Kid" and laugh. Ugh. He felt embarrassed.

But it was worth it. By the end of lunch that day, Jim's backpack was stuffed with wrappers.

It happened again the next day... and the day after that.

On Friday, Rachel and Everett helped Jim count the bundles of wrappers. "I keep losing my place," Everett said.

"Me, too," said Rachel.

"Wait!" Jim said. "I'll get some grocery bags. We can put ten bundles in each bag."

Soon they had filled up four bags. Each bag held 100 wrappers. There were two bundles and five loose wrappers left over.

"425 wrappers!"said Rachel.

"Wow!"said Everett."Your announcement sure did the trick."

Everett is right, thought Jim. It's all about advertising. I've got to spread the word.

And that weekend, he did. He made some flyers. He put one up at the grocery store and left a collection box there. He did the same thing at the Internet Café, the video store, and the health club.

A week later, a woman from the health club called Jim. "Could you please come soon to pick up your wrappers? "she asked. "They're sort of taking over the front desk."

Jim knew the feeling. The wrappers were taking over his room, too.

"Jim,"his mother called. She poked her head in the door."Are you in here?"

"Yeah, Mom,"Jim said. His voice came from somewhere behind the bed.

Jim and his mom carried his wrapper collection to the garage. They got trash bags and put ten grocery bags in each one. When they were done, they had filled six trash bags.

They also had three grocery bags, five bundles and four loose wrappers.

"That's 6354 wrappers!"Jim said.

Saturday afternoon a newspaper reporter rang the doorbell. "Are you Jim, the Blast Off Kid? "she asked."I saw your flyers all over town."

The next morning, Jim opened the newspaper...

And there he was!

Before long, Jim started getting mail. Only six envelopes came the first day.

But the next day there were twelve.

The following week, the mail carrier made a special trip to Jim's house.

His truck was filled with wrappers for the Blast Off Kid!

On Wednesday, Jim's dad was leaving for work. "Has anyone seen the car keys?" he asked. Jim's mom found them in the kitchen.

"Thanks," said Jim's dad. He opened the door to the garage. "Um...has anyone seen the car?" he asked.

"How many wrappers are in here, anyway?" Jim's dad went on. They uncovered the car and started counting.

There were nine trash bags, nine grocery bags, nine bundles, and nine loose wrappers. Jim gasped. "That means..."

Jim ran inside. He got a Grape Blast Off Bar and tore it open.

He added the wrapper to the nine loose wrappers. That was enough to make a bundle. Now he had ten bundles.

He put them into a grocery bag. Now he had ten grocery bags. He put them into a trash bag. Now he had ten trash bags!

"I have 10000 wrappers!" Jim shouted.

Jim's mom called the Blast Off Energy Bar company. A month later, Jim was at space camp!

He wrote a postcard home.

Dear Mom and Dad,

I'm having a blast at space camp...

Today I learned about rockets.

Yesterday I tried a flight simulator.

Tomorrow I'll ride in the low-gravity chair.

Oh, yeah! And I found out that I get a ton of Blast Off Bars to take home. I think I'll share them with everyone who helped me win!

P.S. Please don't throw away any Blast Off Energy Drink bottle caps. I heard they are starting a new contest.

Love, Jim.